Student Skill

PRACTICE BOOK

Developmental Studies Center
2000 Embarcadero, Suite 305
Oakland, CA 94606-5300
(800) 666-7270, fax: (510) 464-3670
www.devstu.org

ISBN-13: 978-1-59892-335-3
ISBN-10: 1-59892-335-8

Printed in the United States of America

1 2 3 4 5 6 7 8 9 10 MLY 11 10 09 08 07

Table of Contents

continues

Table of Contents *continued*

The Smile

A. **Read the passage below. Underline the nouns in one color and the adjectives in another. Add a few adjectives to the passage.**

Mr. South works at the store down the road. He has a grumpy dog named Gerald. Mr. South has angry eyes and a harsh, scratchy voice. Mom says you could scrub an old frying pan with a voice like that.

People say that Mr. South doesn't know how to smile. But when I went to buy bread yesterday, I saw Mr. South patting Gerald. His mouth was curved. His eyes were shining. Then Mr. South saw me. His smile faded. Mom says it was probably all a dream.

B. **Write a short passage using interesting nouns and adjectives. Underline the nouns in one color and the adjectives in another.**

My Friends

A. **Read the passage below. Underline the nouns in one color and the adjectives in another. Add a few adjectives to the passage.**

My friends are as odd as three socks. Mina has long toes.

She used to play the piano with them, but her mom made

her stop.

Consuela is alert and watchful, like an owl. Consuela

imitates every person she meets. So she is also like a talkative

parrot.

Chrissy wears a camera around her neck. She wants to

become a famous filmmaker. Her latest movie is a thriller.

It's about her mom running late for work.

B. **Write a short passage using interesting nouns and adjectives. Underline the nouns in one color and the adjectives in another.**

Locusts

A. **Read the passage below. Underline the nouns in one color and the adjectives in another. Add a few adjectives to the passage.**

Locusts are large insects. They have big heads, silver wings, and long legs. When they're not flying, they sit in fields of plants, eating everything.

Locusts usually travel in big swarms. A swarm of locusts is a scary sight. Sometimes, the swarm blocks out the sun, like a storm cloud. The sound of beating wings is loud. Locusts can turn a field of green plants into a field of bare stalks.

B. **Write a short passage using interesting nouns and adjectives. Underline the nouns in one color and the adjectives in another.**

The African Elephant

A. **Read the passage below. Underline the nouns in one color and the adjectives in another. Add a few adjectives to the passage.**

The African elephant has gray skin with deep, soft wrinkles. Its forehead is smooth and curved. Its ears are shaped a bit like the continent of Africa. It waves them like a fan to keep insects away. An elephant uses its trunk like a hand. It can carry an object as heavy as a tree trunk or as small as a blade of grass. An elephant walks with a steady, lumbering stride—but when it's angry or frightened, it can gallop at about 25 miles per hour.

B. **Write a short passage using interesting nouns and adjectives. Underline the nouns in one color and the adjectives in another.**

Whale Watching

A. **Read the passage below. Underline the verbs in one color and the adverbs in another. Add a couple of adverbs to the passage.**

On my birthday, Dad and I went sailing. The wind was cold and the sky was dark. Seagulls flew above us, and called sadly. I wished I was at home eating ice cream. The sailing trip was Dad's idea.

That was when I saw a smooth, dark shape that curved out of the sea. I saw a huge tail break the surface of the water. It rose up. Then, slowly, the tail slid back into the water. That creature was as big as an island!

B. **Write a short passage using interesting verbs and adverbs. Underline the verbs in one color and the adverbs in another.**

The Trap

A.   Read the passage below. Underline the verbs in one color and the adverbs in another. Add a couple of adverbs to the passage.

The Venus flytrap is a plant that eats flies, spiders, and other bugs. When a fly lands on one of the leaves. The plant swings instantly into action. In a second, two leaves clamp shut over the fly. The fly struggles helplessly, but it can't escape. The plant eats the fly. Soon, the leaves open again. The plant waits patiently for its next victim.

B.   Write a short passage using interesting verbs and adverbs. Underline the verbs in one color and the adverbs in another.

The Attic Song

A.   Read the passage below. Underline the verbs in one color and the adverbs in another. Add a couple of adverbs to the passage.

On the weekend, my brother Thom borrowed a drum from school. He carried the drum carefully up the stairs and into the attic. Suddenly, the walls of our house began to shake and quiver. I looked at Dad. His newspaper shook. Dad muttered gloomily to himself, but I couldn't hear him properly over the noise. I leaped up to get my guitar. I was sure Thom would let me join in. We could start a band in the attic!

B.   Write a short passage using interesting verbs and adverbs. Underline the verbs in one color and the adverbs in another.

Monster of the Deep

A. **Read the passage below. Underline the verbs in one color and the adverbs in another. Add a couple of adverbs to the passage.**

It was November 1861. A boat sailed near the Canary Islands. Suddenly, the crew saw something unusual. They saw long, fleshy arms that trailed through the water. They saw a huge body and eyes as big as dinner plates. The crew panicked. They fired guns. They threw spears. Finally, they tied a rope around the monster's tail. They tried desperately to pull the creature on board. But the creature slipped into the sea.

B. **Write a short passage using interesting verbs and adverbs. Underline the verbs in one color and the adverbs in another.**

Whose Lizard?

A. **Read the passage below. Underline personal pronouns in one color and possessive pronouns in another.**

On pet day, people brought their birds, turtles, and rats

to school. I brought Allen.

"Whose lizard is this?" Mr. Berry said when he discovered

Allen hiding in the curtains. He looked a little scared.

My classmates pointed at me.

B. **Read the passage below. Write the correct pronoun in each blank.**

"That's not _____ lizard," _____ said

quickly, denying all responsibility.

When I got home, Mom kissed Allen on the head.

_____ loves her lizard.

C. **Write a short passage using at least three of the possessive pronouns below.**

my   your   her   his   our   their   its

Vegetables

A. **Read the passage below. Underline personal pronouns in one color and possessive pronouns in another.**

Our neighbors have a vegetable garden just like ours.

They have spinach, zucchini, and broccoli, like we have.

They have squash, too, but their squash are growing faster

than ours.

B. **Read the passage below. Write the correct pronoun in each blank.**

"This is terrible!" Mom said, pointing at a squash. "This

squash hasn't grown at all."

"None of _____ likes squash, anyway," Dad said to

Mom.

"Maybe it feels bad," said Mom. "_____ knows no

one likes _____."

C. **Write a short passage using at least three of the possessive pronouns below.**

my   your   her   his   our   their   its

In the Morning

A. **Read the passage below. Underline personal pronouns in one color and possessive pronouns in another.**

Dad came storming into the bedroom. "Whose is this?"

he demanded, holding up a wet towel.

AJ and I looked at each other. "Not mine," we both said.

"Somebody left it on the bathroom floor," said Dad.

B. **Read the passage below. Write the correct pronoun in each blank.**

"It must be _____," I told AJ. "I haven't had

_____ shower yet."

AJ frowned at me. "I haven't had _____ either!" he said.

Dad stared at _____. "Maybe it was the cat," he

said wearily.

C. **Write a short passage using at least three of the possessive pronouns below.**

my   your   her   his   our   their   its

Pancakes

A. **Read the passage below. Underline personal pronouns in one color and possessive pronouns in another.**

Yesterday, Astrid and I made pancakes. For some reason, my pancakes turned out better than Astrid's pancakes. When all the pancakes were ready, she took the ones I had made! I was left with her lumpy ones.

B. **Read the passage below. Write the correct pronoun in each blank.**

"Hey," I said, "you didn't make _____."

"It doesn't matter," Astrid said. "_____ will all taste the same."

"But…the pancakes on your plate are _____," I said.

"Not any more," Astrid said as she squirted maple syrup all over _____.

C. **Write a short passage using at least three of the possessive pronouns below.**

my   your   her   his   our   their   its

The Trap-door Spider

A.   Read the passage below. Underline prepositions in one color and prepositional phrases in another.

The trap-door spider is a master of surprise. Its home is a hole deep in the ground. The spider builds a trapdoor over its home. The trapdoor is made from mud and has hinges made from silk.

The spider waits patiently behind the door until an insect walks past its home. Suddenly, the spider bursts through the trapdoor. It grabs the insect. Then it drags the insect into the hole. The trapdoor slams shut.

B.   Write a few sentences using at least four of the prepositions below. Underline prepositional phrases in the sentences.

above	across	against	around
behind	below	beneath	beside
between	beyond	inside	near
on	outside	over	under

The Skydiver

A.   **Read the passage below. Underline prepositions in one color and prepositional phrases in another.**

The airplane climbs high into the sky until the earth is below it. The skydiver can see towns, rivers, and the ocean. He thinks of the moment when he will jump. He will dive through the open air. The skydiver looks away from the window. His heart feels like it is about to jump out of his chest. Soon, he will be tumbling through the air.

B.   **Write a few sentences using at least four of the prepositions below. Underline prepositional phrases in the sentences.**

above	across	against	around
behind	below	beneath	beside
between	beyond	inside	near
on	outside	over	under

The Invasion

A. Read the passage below. Underline prepositions in one color and prepositional phrases in another.

At lunchtime, Yuko and Rashida filled a picnic basket with donuts. They strolled across a bridge, stopped under a tree, and spread a blanket over the grass. Before long, they were both stretched out in the shade, asleep.

When they woke up, an army of ants was marching down the tree. The army was heading toward the picnic basket. They were eating tunnels through the donuts.

Rashida and Yuko looked at each other. They shrugged. They pulled their sun hats over their faces and went back to sleep.

B. Write a few sentences using at least four of the prepositions below. Underline prepositional phrases in the sentences.

above	across	against	around
behind	below	beneath	beside
between	beyond	inside	near
on	outside	over	under

A Quiet Life

A. **Read the passage below. Underline prepositions in one color and prepositional phrases in another.**

A hermit is a person who lives alone, away from other

people. He or she may feel uncomfortable being near others.

Or the person might just feel happy living a simple, quiet

life. Hermits have existed since ancient times. One ancient

Greek hermit lived in a barrel. Legend has it that when a

king came to visit the hermit and offered to grant him one

wish, the hermit wished for the king to go away.

B. **Write a few sentences using at least four of the prepositions below. Underline prepositional phrases in the sentences.**

above	across	against	around
behind	below	beneath	beside
between	beyond	inside	near
on	outside	over	under

Up the Hill

A.   Read the passage below. Divide the run-on sentences.

The worst part of my bike ride home from school is the last bend that's where the road climbs a steep hill I push my feet against the pedals and begin to climb my muscles start to burn and my shoulders begin to ache sweat gathers inside my helmet and drips into my eyes I pedal and pedal until my lungs are about to explode I must be near the top by now but I can't slow down I just have to keep going inch by inch until I get there.

B.   Read the very long sentence below. Divide it into shorter sentences. Look for words like *and*, *so*, and *then* to help you divide the sentence.

My mom and sister and I live at the top of the steepest hill in town and when you're biking up the hill, it looks as though our house is right on the edge of the world then when you get there, you see that the world just keeps going all the way past our house So my sister says we're lucky to live where we do because if there's a big flood we will be safe and I suppose she has a point.

Mighty Mold

A.   Read the passage below. Divide the run-on sentences.

Mold grows on things like bread it is white it looks soft and furry hopefully, you won't discover the mold when you are eating a sandwich hopefully, you will discover it before you take the first bite.

B.   Read the very long sentence below. Divide it into shorter sentences. Look for words like *and*, *so*, and *then* to help you divide the sentence.

One of the world's most important medicines comes from mold and it is called penicillin and it was discovered by a man named Alexander Fleming then Fleming left a dish of germs near a window and mold grew in the dish so Fleming was about to throw the dish away but then he looked closely so he saw that the mold had eaten the germs.

Coffee

A.   Read the passage below. Divide the run-on sentences.

My older brother loves coffee I wanted to know why he likes it so much, so the other day he brewed some fresh coffee and poured me a cup it smelled really good I took a huge gulp it tasted like melted tar I managed to swallow it but it took three days to get the taste out of my mouth I can't believe my brother drinks that stuff.

B.   Read the very long sentence below. Divide it into shorter sentences. Look for words like *and*, *so*, and *then* to help you divide the sentence.

My brother says that your tastes change as you get older and he says that coffee could end up being my favorite drink, but I don't believe him because ever since he went to college, he pretends to know everything so all that coffee must be affecting his brain and *something* is, anyway.

No Water

A. Read the passage below. Divide the run-on sentences.

A drought is when there is no rain for a long time. In a drought the water in rivers and wells dries up farm animals suffer and plants die fires erupt easily in forests and they spread quickly deep cracks form in the ground as though the earth is gasping for water people must use every drop of water carefully and hope that rain will fall.

B. Read the very long sentence below. Divide it into shorter sentences. Look for words like *and*, *so*, and *then* to help you divide the sentence.

It's difficult to know when a drought will happen however scientists have found that dry times often follow rainy times and they can trace dry times and rainy times by looking at how fast trees have grown because in rainy years trees grow fast and in dry years trees grow slower.

Sentence Pairs

A. **Turn each sentence into two, short sentences.**

My best friend, a soccer player, taught me how to play soccer.

My best friend _____

My best friend _____

Poodles, a breed of dog, are favorite family pets.

_____

_____

B. **Combine each pair of sentences into a single sentence, as shown.**

Feelings are normal.

Feelings can help you make decisions.

Feelings, which are normal, can help you make decisions.

My parents are standing in the back row.

My parents are waving.

_____

Sentence Pairs

A.   Turn each sentence into two, short sentences.

My teacher, a native Chinese speaker, taught me how to

speak Chinese.

My teacher _____

My teacher _____

Tae Kwon Do, a Korean martial art, requires focus and discipline.

_____

_____

B.   Combine each pair of sentences into a single sentence, as shown.

The mountain is too dangerous to climb.

The mountain is cold and steep.

The mountain, cold and steep, is too dangerous to climb.

The dog is barking loudly.

The dog is driving me mad.

_____

Sentence Pairs

A.   Turn each sentence into two, short sentences.

My cousin, a juggler, knows how to juggle eight oranges.

My cousin _____

My cousin _____

My favorite T-shirt, the one with the holes, needs to be washed.

_____

_____

B.   Combine each pair of sentences into a single sentence, as shown.

The baby is making a lot of noise.

The baby is not my sister.

The baby making a lot of noise is not my sister. _____

My favorite food is fresh bread.

My favorite food is easy to make when you know how.

_____

_____

Sentence Pairs

A. **Turn each sentence into two, short sentences.**

My aunt, a carpenter, builds her own furniture.

My aunt _____

My aunt _____

My favorite flavor, chocolate, is everyone else's favorite, too.

_____

_____

B. **Combine each pair of sentences into a single sentence, as shown.**

My grandmother is a great piano player.

My grandmother taught me how to read music.

My grandmother, a great piano player, taught me
how to read music.

The boy is playing the guitar.

The boy is my brother.

_____

The Pear Tree

A. **Read the passage below. Replace the misused words with correct words.**

Their is a pear tree across the fence. It is a monster of a pair tree. It must be thirty feet high! The problem is that my neighbors and I can't agree who's tree it is.

"Its my tree," says my neighbor, "because its growing on my side of the fence."

I think the tree belongs to me because it leans over the fence. I like to set down underneath the tree. I stretch out and lay in the shade, surrounded by the cent of pairs.

B. **Choose any three words from the sets of words below and write a short passage using the words correctly.**

to/too/two   there/their/they're

who's/whose   its/it's

your/you're

Running Away

A. **Read the passage below. Replace the misused words with correct words.**

On the morning we ran away from home, Sonia and I climbed a hill. We watched the sun raise.

"What should we do today?" Sonia asked.

"We could visit the mall," I said. "We could check out the clothing sails!"

Sonia raised her eyebrows. "Great idea," she said, "accept people will see us and tell our parents that we've run away."

We had been on the run for only a few ours, and I missed home all ready.

B. **Choose any three words from the sets of words below and write a short passage using the words correctly.**

to/too/two   there/their/they're

who's/whose   its/it's

your/you're

Earth's Fireworks

A.   Read the passage below. Replace the misused words with correct words.

A volcano is like a fireworks display put on by Earth. Huge clouds of fire shoot out of the mountain. Rivers of burning rock slide down it's sides. Hot ash pours out of the mountaintop and chunks of rock are throne high into the air. If the volcano is strong enough, it could blow the hole mountain to pieces.

B.   Choose any three words from the sets of words below and write a short passage using the words correctly.

to/too/two	there/their/they're
who's/whose	its/it's
your/you're	

Frida Kahlo

A. Read the passage below. Replace the misused words with correct words.

Frida Kahlo was a Mexican artist. She wanted too become a doctor. But when she was fifteen, she was hurt in a terrible bus crash. She wasn't able too study medicine, so she taught herself two paint. She didn't paint exactly what she saw. Instead, she painted things she imagined. In one painting, their are too Fridas sitting together.

B. Choose any three words from the sets of words below and write a short passage using the words correctly.

to/too/two   there/their/they're

who's/whose   its/it's

your/you're

The Artists

A.   Read the passage below and underline the verbs.

On Sunday mornings, my brother Jake spreads newspaper over the dining table and paints. My sister Winona scribbles poems in her notebook. I cut pictures out of magazines and arrange them on my bedroom wall. Dad switches on the stereo and dances around the kitchen. He sings loudly as he makes lunch.

B.   Read the passage below with the new people added. Underline the verbs and correct them, if necessary.

On Sunday mornings, my mom and my brother Jake spreads newspaper over the dining table and paints. My sister Winona and her friend Nelly scribbles poems in their notebooks. My friend Ramona and I cut pictures out of magazines and arrange them on my bedroom wall. Dad and Grandma switches on the stereo and dances around the kitchen. They sings loudly as they makes lunch.

On the Weekend

A. **Read the passage below and underline the verbs.**

On the weekend, Sam travels up the Amazon River. Unfortunately, he forgets insect repellent. As mosquitoes eat him alive, Sam abandons his boat and swims up the river instead. Some stingrays, pink dolphins, piranhas, and crocodiles keep him company as he swims.

B. **Read the passage below with the new people added. Underline the verbs and correct them, if necessary.**

On the weekend, Sam and his friend Kat travels up the Amazon River. Unfortunately, they forgets insect repellent. As mosquitoes eat them alive, Sam and Kat abandons their boat and swims up the river instead. Some stingrays, pink dolphins, piranhas, and crocodiles keep them company as they swims.

Camping with Lionel

A.   Read the passage below and underline the verbs.

On the first day, it rains. There are leaks in our cabin. My friend Lionel dashes around. He puts salad bowls under all the leaks. Lionel's sister Joanne covers the furniture with sheets. I do, too. Mrs. Darby stands on a chair and seals the leaks with sticky tape.

B.   Read the passage below with the new people added. Underline the verbs and correct them, if necessary.

On the first day, it rains. There are leaks in our cabin. My friend Lionel and I dashes around. We puts salad bowls under all the leaks. Lionel's sisters Joanne and Chelsea covers the furniture with sheets. I do, too. Mr. and Mrs. Darby stands on chairs and seals the leaks with sticky tape.

All That Jazz

A.   **Read the passage below and underline the verbs.**

You hear many different sounds when you listen to a band. A drummer plays the rhythm. Three saxophones play the song. A clarinet climbs up and down the scale. The players' fingers move very fast.

B.   **Read the passage below with the new people added. Underline the verbs and correct them, if necessary.**

You hear many different sounds when you listen to a band. A drummer and a percussionist plays the rhythm. Three saxophones and a trombone plays the song. A clarinet and a flute climbs up and down the scale. The players' fingers move very fast.

Who Is Louis Sachar?

A. **Read the passage below. Underline the verbs and mark if they are in past (*pa*), present (*pr*), or future (*f*) tense, as shown below.**

pa
Louis Sachar <u>was</u> born in New York in 1954. When he was nine, his family moved to California. Orange trees grew all around. Louis and his friends had fights with the mushy, rotten fruit underneath the trees.

Today, Louis Sachar dreams up crazy ideas for children's books. He says that it is a thrill to start with a blank page and finish with a whole story. Louis keeps his stories secret until he writes the very last word.

Louis might write a book for adults one day. His adult characters probably won't have the same kinds of adventures as his young characters, but hopefully, the stories will be just as action-packed.

B. **Write three short paragraphs like those above using past, present, and future verb tenses.**

Summers

A. **Read the passage below. Underline the verbs and mark if they are in past (*pa*), present (*pr*), or future (*f*) tense, as shown below.**

                                    pa

Years ago, my family and I <u>spent</u> summers at Granddad's place. Dad usually disappeared into the woods with his *Field Guide for Birds* book. Mom collected plants. I hung out in the barn with my big brother as he took Granddad's old cars to pieces.

Now that my brother is gone, we go to the lake. Mom and Dad lie on the sand and swat sandflies. I swim. Everything is boring without my brother.

One day, I will leave home and my parents will go on great holidays again. They will sigh with relief. "Finally, we will go somewhere really amazing," Mom will say.

B. **Write three short paragraphs like those above using past, present, and future verb tenses.**

How Will We Travel?

A.   Read the passage below. Underline the verbs and mark if they are in past (*pa*), present (*pr*), or future (*f*) tense, as shown below.

                                                      pa
Long, long ago, people traveled only on foot. They

hoisted loads onto their backs, balanced them on their heads,

or dragged them along the ground. About 5000 BC, people

strapped loads to the backs of animals.

Today, on a jet airliner, travelers move as fast as the

speed of sound. Trains, trucks, and cargo ships haul goods all

over the globe. Millions of people watch the world flash by

from inside cars, buses, and trains.

In the future, maybe the trains will hover above the

ground. Maybe cars will drive themselves. Perhaps no one

will walk anymore.

B.   Write three short paragraphs like those above using past, present, and future verb tenses.

Fearless

A.   **Read the passage below. Underline the verbs and mark if they are in past (*pa*), present (*pr*), or future (*f*) tense, as shown below.**

                        pa

Once, I <u>was frightened</u> of the dark. I thought that

the dark swallowed people who closed their eyes. So my

dad bought me a night lamp. It glowed beside my bed.

Somehow, it helped me see that the dark was not as scary

as it looked.

    I am not afraid of the dark anymore, but now I feel

nervous about the future. I worry about many things. People

think I am fearless, but that is not true.

    Perhaps one day, I will overcome my fears. Perhaps they

will fade and will become nothing more than shadows.

B.   **Write three short paragraphs like those above using past, present, and future verb tenses.**

Summer Camp

A. **Read the passage below. Is it written from the first, second, or third person point of view?**

When you were eight, you went to camp for the first time. You heard that kids were left by themselves in the woods for three days with no food, tent, or toilet paper. On the first day, all the kids went to a park. You were scared. But, everyone went on a picnic. You and your friends looked up at the clouds and described the shapes you could see. It was actually kind of fun.

Point of view: _____

B. **Rewrite the passage above from a different point of view.**

C. **Write a short passage from the point of view that was not used in step A or B.**

Dreams

A. **Read the passage below. Is it written from the first, second, or third person point of view?**

Damien has been having strange dreams. Last night, he dreamed that he was arm wrestling with a giant fish. The night before that, Damien dreamed that he had swallowed a balloon. He was taking a math test, but he kept floating out of his chair and bumping his head on the ceiling. "Sit down," his teacher said. "You're bothering the class." Damien was about to get in big trouble, but luckily, he woke up.

Point of view: _____

B. **Rewrite the passage above from a different point of view.**

C. **Write a short passage from the point of view that was not used in step A or B.**

George

A. **Read the passage below. Is it written from the first, second, or third person point of view?**

When Mrs. Munro says that our class is going to have a talent show, I make a face. I don't have an amazing talent. However, I *do* have George. George is my puppet. He is a monkey puppet. On talent show day, George and I swallow our fear. I put my favorite song on the stereo and George begins to dance. He dances as though he's been performing all his life. At the end, we twirl across the stage together. We're a hit!

Point of view: _____

B. **Rewrite the passage above from a different point of view.**

C. **Write a short passage from the point of view that was not used in step A or B.**

The Three-Legged Race

A. **Read the passage below. Is it written from the first, second, or third person point of view?**

Sam and Jacob enter the three-legged race in their classroom Olympics. Jacob ties his right ankle to Sam's left ankle. They practice hobbling around together. At first, Jacob loses his balance and they both fall in a heap. But they get better with practice. When the race starts, Sam and Jacob shuffle forward. Suddenly, Jacob feels annoyed. Sam is holding him back! Jacob bends down and unties his ankle. "I'm free," he yells. He dashes for the finish line, laughing and waving his arms.

Point of view: _____

B. **Rewrite the passage above from a different point of view.**

C. **Write a short passage from the point of view that was not used in step A or B.**

Route 66

A.   Read the passage below, and then write the main idea of each paragraph.

U.S. Route 66 is a famous highway in America. It opened in 1926. It linked Chicago and Los Angeles. Some people called it the "Main Street of America." If you lived in a small town, Route 66 was your link to a big city.

Main idea: _____

In the 1950s, people began building freeways so that they could travel faster. Slowly, parts of Route 66 were replaced with new freeways. Route 66 was never the same.

Main idea: _____

B.   Insert a paragraph symbol (¶) below wherever a new paragraph should begin.

People still like to travel on old Route 66. They eat in old diners and stay in roadside motels. They visit museums and other sights along the way. Today, there are companies that take people on tours of Route 66. You can even take a tour by motorcycle!

Big Bad Wolves

A. **Read the passage below, and then write the main idea of each paragraph.**

Many people are afraid of wolves. Wolves are dangerous in many stories. In "Little Red Riding Hood," a wolf threatens to eat a little girl. In "The Three Little Pigs," a wolf bullies three helpless pigs.

Main idea: _____

The truth is, wolves are very shy. They live in places where there are not a lot of people. They usually run when they see or smell people.

Main idea: _____

B. **Insert a paragraph symbol (¶) below wherever a new paragraph should begin.**

People's fear of wolves has led them to kill them. In the past, the U.S. government encouraged people to kill wolves. Sadly, so many wolves have been killed that some kinds are in danger of disappearing forever. For example, the red wolf and the grey wolf are nearly extinct in the U.S.

My Brother Tristan

A.   Read the passage below, and then write the main idea of each paragraph.

My brother Tristan and I fight a lot. He is very stubborn. He's also funny and smart, but I forget that when we fight. So far, I think we have had about a million fights.

Main idea: _____

Yesterday we had a fight over raspberry jello. Tristan finished his jello and wanted mine. When I said "No," he stuck his chubby hand right into my bowl! I was mad!

Main idea: _____

B.   Insert a paragraph symbol (¶) below wherever a new paragraph should begin.

For a long time, Tristan and I fought over objects. We fought about toys. We fought about books. We fought about food. Now, our fights are different. For example, yesterday we had a fight about which kind of dog we like. Our fights are more like talking now, but with more shouting.

Desert Life

A.   Read the passage below, and then write the main idea of each paragraph.

In the desert, the only place with water is an oasis. An oasis is a place in the desert with a spring. In large deserts, like the Sahara, people build towns near oases.

Main idea: _____

Desert animals use oases, too. Gazelles, antelope, snakes, and small foxes get water from the oasis. They also eat the plants that grow there.

Main idea: _____

B.   Insert a paragraph symbol (¶) below wherever a new paragraph should begin.

If you visited the Sahara Desert ten thousand years ago, you would not know it was a desert. Back then, the Sahara had lakes, streams, grass, and trees. People and animals lived there. But, about six thousand years ago, the Sahara became hotter and drier. Eventually, the Sahara became so dry that very few people or animals lived there anymore.

Dragons

A. **Read the following paragraph. What do you notice about the underlined words?**

A dragon is an imaginary animal <u>that</u> many cultures have stories about. <u>While</u> many European stories show dragons as frightening and ugly, many Asian stories show dragons as neither frightening <u>nor</u> ugly. <u>Instead</u>, they represent good luck!

B. **Use some of the following conjunctions to connect ideas in the paragraph below:** *and, after, although, as, because, before, but, for, how, however, if, nor, once, or, since, so, than, though, until, when, where, whether, while, yet.*

In China, people are building a giant dragon sculpture. It will curve along the ridge of a mountain. The dragon's head will be 100 feet high. Its body will be 30 feet high Its body will be 20 feet wide. It will be covered in nearly six million pieces of marble and bronze. These pieces will form scales. The scales will represent the many different cultures of China.

The Bicycle Club

A. **Read the following paragraph. What do you notice about the underlined words?**

If you want to join my bicycle club, your bicycle must have a name. Bike or Cycle is not a good name. However, a name like Torpedo or Meteor would be better, although the name should always mean something to you personally.

B. **Use some of the following conjunctions to connect ideas in the paragraph below:** *and, after, although, as, because, before, but, for, how, however, if, nor, once, or, since, so, than, though, until, when, where, whether, while, yet.*

I started a bicycle club. I've always thought that bicycles are wonderful. They'll take you almost anywhere you want to go. Did you know that there are about one billion bicycles in the world? That is more than twice the number of cars. It's much more exciting to ride a bicycle than to ride in a car. You experience the journey more!

Making Music

A. **Read the following paragraph. What do you notice about the underlined words?**

Before you decide which musical instrument you'd like to play, do some research. Although instruments like the saxophone are fun, there are lots of cool instruments out there. You may have tried the trumpet, but have you tried a trombone? Once you've learned how to play the piano, you should try the electric keyboard.

B. **Use some of the following conjunctions to connect ideas in the paragraph below:** *and, after, although, as, because, before, but, for, how, however, if, nor, once, or, since, so, than, though, until, when, where, whether, while, yet.*

The Treholipee is an odd-looking musical instrument. It was invented in the 1960s. It was popular for a very short time. You won't see many of them around today. Its body looks like a small guitar. Its neck is long and curved.

Inventions

A. Read the following paragraph. What do you notice about the underlined words?

Experiments can be exciting, <u>but</u> they can also lead to unexpected results. I know this <u>because</u> I do lots of experiments <u>as</u> an inventor. I am working on an invention <u>that</u> will make people taller. <u>Since</u> I have not invented it yet, I can't tell you how it will work.

B. Use some of the following conjunctions to connect ideas in the paragraph below: *and, after, although, as, because, before, but, for, how, however, if, nor, once, or, since, so, than, though, until, when, where, whether, while, yet.*

Ideas for inventions are all around. It's simply a matter of looking for ways to make things better. Imagine that something annoys you, imagine how you might solve the problem. You might get annoyed when you lose your socks. You could invent flashing lights to go on your socks. Now they'll be easy to find.

Sun and Storm

A.   Add single or double quotation marks to the dialogue, as shown below.

My aunt Jen used to live in Japan. One of her favorite Japanese stories is the one about the sun.

"Once, there was a girl named Sun," Aunt Jen tells my brother and me. "She was so dazzling that her parents said, 'Why don't we put her in the sky?'"

Then Aunt Jen tells how Sun went to live in the sky where she gave warmth and light to plants and animals on Earth. She was a total superstar. But Sun also had a brother named Storm.

Storm was a control freak, Aunt Jen explains. He liked being in charge. He stomped around making valleys with his feet and tearing up trees with his breath.

He sounds like you! I tell my brother.

B.   Write a brief dialogue that includes single and double quotation marks.

Not-so-scary Stories

A. **Add single or double quotation marks to the dialogue, as shown below.**

When I was small, my mom would try to tell me scary stories. She would sit beside my bed, holding a flashlight under her chin to make her look like a ghost.

"It was a dark and stormy night," Mom said. "A boy named Elroy couldn't sleep."

Why not? I asked.

Because the wind was making a strange sound outside his window, Mom said. It sounded as though it was saying, El-roy… El-roy…

I don't like this story, I said.

Wait until you hear what happens, said Mom. Elroy got up and went to the window. He heard the wind say, Hey, Elroy! It's cold out. Let me in.

This is not a scary story, I said.

B. **Write a brief dialogue that includes single and double quotation marks.**

Eileen

A. **Add single or double quotation marks to the dialogue, as shown below.**

My friend Dave has a baby sister named Eileen. She makes noises, but doesn't talk yet. Dave is pretty good at figuring out what she's saying.

"When she yells, it means she's tired, but it can mean other stuff, too," Dave explained to me. "One time, it meant, 'Hey, Dave, let's build a spaceship!' So we built this awesome spaceship in the living room."

Just then, Eileen started howling. Dave's mom picked her up and said, This one's easy. She's saying, Feed me.

No, she's not, Dave said. She's saying, I'm bored. Let's go to the movies.

Dave's mom frowned. How do you know?

I just know, Dave said.

B. **Write a brief dialogue that includes single and double quotation marks.**

Waldo the Great

A. Add single or double quotation marks to the dialogue, as shown below.

Yesterday, I helped my neighbor Mr. Kite take his dog Waldo for a walk. We were about to cross a bridge when Waldo came to a stop.

"Oh no! He always does this,"Mr. Kite groaned.

I bent down and said, What's up, Waldo? Is there a bad smell around here?

Waldo woofed softly and showed the whites of his eyes.

Maybe he's saying, My legs are sore, I told Mr. Kite.

Mr. Kite shook his head. I know what the problem is, he said. Waldo is saying, I can't stand heights, water, or fish, and I won't cross the bridge unless somebody carries me.

I sighed and said, OK. I picked up Waldo and tucked him under my arm.

B. Write a brief dialogue that includes single and double quotation marks.

Spring

A. **Read the first paragraph and notice how the commas are used in a series. Then add the missing commas to the second paragraph.**

Every spring, I do spring cleaning. This is the kind of cleaning that makes your hands wrinkle, your back ache, and your eyes water. I dust off the carpet, polish the computer, and scrub the floor. I clean the bathroom, wash the bathtub, polish the taps, and sweep the floor.

Then I wash the curtains wipe down the walls and stand on a ladder to mop the ceiling. I rescue all the spiders caterpillars and cockroaches and put them in the garden. I dust every leaf of my indoor plants. I have five angel ivy trees twenty ponytail palm trees and six Chinese evergreen trees. Finally, I wash the dog the cat and the gerbil. Everything is clean!

B. **Write a paragraph using commas in a series.**

How to Name a Pet

A. **Read the first paragraph and notice how the commas are used in a series. Then add the missing commas to the second paragraph.**

It's hard to name a pet. There are so many choices. Lots of people name their dog Rover, Sam, or Max. Many people name their cat Blackie, Tiger, or Ginger. But pets can also have names like Bob, Ralph, or Margaret.

I think the best way to name your pet is to look at it carefully. My dog has black fur. I thought about naming him Shadow Smokey or Bandit. He loves to run. I thought of Runner Speedy and Jumper. Finally, I decided on Buster. I think he looks like a Buster.

B. **Write a paragraph using commas in a series.**

Mohammed's Story

A. **Read the first paragraph and notice how the commas are used in a series. Then add the missing commas to the second paragraph.**

I was born in West Africa. I came to the United States because I wanted to go to school. Education is very important to me. My grandparents, my parents, and my brothers and sisters never had a chance to go to school. Leaving West Africa was hard. The day I left, my friends and family gathered together, took pictures, and said goodbye.

My life is so different now! Everything I see hear touch and taste is new. I've learned new words new sports and new ideas. I've eaten new foods like waffles bagels and granola. I've found new friends new traditions and a new home.

B. **Write a paragraph using commas in a series.**

Picnic Ingredients

A. Read the first paragraph and notice how the commas are used in a series. Then add the missing commas to the second paragraph.

What do you need for a great picnic? Delicious food, good friends, and a rug to sit on are great. A sunny day is also a good thing. You might want to wait if there's rain, hail, or snow on the way.

Let's say it's a sunny day. Pack some food into a bag basket or box. Sandwiches salads cakes and cookies are all excellent. Don't forget something to drink. If you plan to walk through a park climb a hill or go exploring you'll get thirsty. Other things to take include a map a camera and a few friends.

B. Write a paragraph using commas in a series.

New Year's in Thailand

A. **Read the following passages and capitalize letters where needed, as shown below.**

In ~~t~~hailand, the new year starts in april. It is a time

of cleaning and new life. One tradition is to throw water.

People use hoses and water pistols to drench one another.

People carry buddhist statues through the streets so that

passersby can splash them with water.

B. **For each word you capitalized, write the type of proper noun it is, as shown below.**

- names of countries
- names of religions

C. **Choose two different types of proper nouns from the list above. Write five examples for each type, as shown.**

- names of religions: Buddhism, Christianity, Islam, Hinduism, Judaism

Japanese New Year's

A. **Read the following passages and capitalize letters where needed, as shown below.**

J
japanese people celebrate the new year on january 1.

The celebration is similar to christmas. People send one

another cards, sing songs, and eat lots of food. japanese

children are given money in a tradition called "otoshidama"

that came from china. On new year's day, people celebrate

the first things of the year. They watch the first sunrise and

celebrate the first smile they see.

B. **For each word you capitalized, write the type of proper noun it is, as shown below.**

- names of ethnicities
  or nationalities
- names of languages

C. **Choose two different types of proper nouns from the list above. Write five examples for each type, as shown.**

- nationalities: Japanese, South African, Italian,
  Pakistani, Australian

Rosh Hashanah

A. **Read the following passages and capitalize letters where needed, as shown below.**

R
~~R~~osh hashanah is the jewish new year celebration.

The hebrew words "rosh hashanah" mean "beginning of

the year," though the holiday usually begins in september.

When it begins, people blow a trumpet made from a ram's

horn to alert people that the year has begun. Otherwise,

rosh hashanah is a very quiet holiday. People say prayers,

recite poetry, and eat traditional foods like apples and honey.

B. **For each word you capitalized, write the type of proper noun it is, as shown below.**

- names of holidays
- names of languages

C. **Choose two different types of proper nouns from the list above. Write five examples for each type, as shown.**

- names of languages: English, Chinese, Arabic, Swahili, Yiddish

Spanish

A. **Read the following passages and capitalize letters where needed, as shown below.**

S
~~s~~panish is the second most common language in

the united states after english. In 2000, there were

28.1 million people in the u.s. who spoke spanish most

frequently at home. About half of all spanish speakers

also spoke english fluently.

B. **For each word you capitalized, write the type of proper noun it is, as shown below.**

 - names of languages

C. **Choose two different types of proper nouns from the list above. Write five examples for each type, as shown.**

 - names of languages: English, Chinese, Arabic, Swahili, Yiddish

Book Citations

A. **Read the book citations below, and then fill in the blanks with the missing information.**

Gaff, Jackie, and David Jefferis. *Skiing and Snow Sports.*

London: Kingfisher, 1989.

Lennard, Duncan. *Extreme Golf: The World's Most*

Unusual, Fantastic, and Bizarre Courses. New York, NY :

Sourcebooks, 2004.

Shaw, Phil. *Extreme Ironing.* London: New Holland, 2003.

A book citation consists of:

_____ , Author's first name.

_____ . City where published, State:

_____ , _____ .

B. **Write three citations using books of your own.**

Book Citations

A. **Read the book citations below, and then fill in the blanks with the missing information.**

Moses, Brian. *Munching, Crunching, Sniffing and Snooping.*

London: Dorling Kindersley, 1999.

Schubert, Dieter. *Animality*. London: Hutchinson Children's

Books, 1995.

Windham, Ryder. *What You Don't Know About Animals.*

New York, NY: Scholastic, 2002.

A book citation consists of:

Author's last name, _____ .

_____ . _____ ,

_____ : Publisher, _____ .

B. **Write three citations using books of your own.**

Magazine Article Citations

A. Read the magazine citations below, and then fill in the blanks with the missing information.

Margolis, Mac. "Reefs." *Newsweek*, October 2006: pp. 32–34.

Montaigne, Fern, Randy Olson and Brian Skerry. "Still

Waters." *National Geographic*, April 2007: pp. 9–15.

Walker, Gabrielle. "Hidden Antarctica: What Lies Beneath."

New Scientist, December 2006: pp. 14–20.

A magazine citation consists of:

Author's last name, _____ .

" _____ ." _____ ,

Month and year article was published: _____ .

B. Write three citations using magazine articles of your own choice.

Magazine Article Citations

A. **Read the magazine citations below, and then fill in the blanks with the missing information.**

Hardy, Jeffrey. "Underground: The First Subways." *Carfree Living,* January 1999: pp. 25–31.

Alessandro, Greer. "Is Public Transit Making a Comeback?" *Environment Weekly,* June 2004: pp 18–29.

Uddin, Nasim. "Rediscovery: Gandhi's Train Journey." *Train History Magazine,* October 2005: pp. 31–38.

A magazine citation consists of:

_____, _____.

"Title of article." *Title of magazine in italics,*

_____: Page numbers.

B. **Write three citations using magazines articles of your own choice.**

Wild Stories

A. Read the paragraph below and notice how the parentheses are used.

Calamity Jane (1852–1903) was the nickname of a woman named Martha Jane Cannary (or Canary). She was born in Princeton, Missouri, and grew up in Virginia City, Montana. She learned to ride a horse and she dressed in men's clothes (usually a cowboy jacket and an old hat). She chewed tobacco, and she was handy with a gun, too.

B. Read the paragraph below and add parentheses where appropriate.

Some say that Calamity Jane once swam 90 miles 145 kilometers up the Platte River. Others tell stories of how she was thrown out of many towns usually for shooting up the saloon. One story has it that Calamity Jane pulled two guns on some cowboys in a saloon in North Dakota she aimed at their feet and told them to dance for their lives.

C. Write a short passage using parentheses.

The Library

A. Read the paragraph below and notice how the parentheses are used.

The library is a quiet place. It's against the rules to talk in a loud voice. If I speak too loudly, Mr. Ernest (the school librarian) gets angry. But I'm the kind of person who likes to talk out loud. If I read something funny (like a comic book), I like to read it out loud, so that everyone can hear.

B. Read the paragraph below and add parentheses where appropriate.

If there is any sound Mr. Ernest likes less than talking, it's laughing he doesn't like singing much, either. As you know, laughter is contagious it spreads like the flu. Once I start laughing, I get all my friends laughing and in trouble too.

C. Write a short passage using parentheses.

Paul Bunyan, Man of Mystery

A. Read the paragraph below and notice how the parentheses are used.

Paul Bunyan was not a real person, but he was the hero of many stories. He was a giant and a lumberjack (a person who cuts down trees for lumber). It is said that he and his blue ox (named Babe) were so large that their footsteps created Minnesota's ten thousand lakes.

B. Read the paragraph below and add parentheses where appropriate.

In the early 1900s, James MacGillivray a young newspaper reporter told the first stories about Paul Bunyan. Some of these stories included other characters, like Dutch Jake another lumberjack and Sailor Jake Paul Bunyan's enemy. Today, there are statues of Paul Bunyan all over America. One is in Oscoda, Michigan said to be his first home.

C. Write a short passage using parentheses.

The Painter

A. **Read the paragraph below and notice how the parentheses are used.**

My neighbor Henry is a painter. He wants to paint like Pablo Picasso (an artist who painted people with extremely odd faces). Henry also likes paintings by Vincent Van Gogh (who loved to paint sunflowers) and Marc Chagall (whose favorite color was blue).

B. **Read the paragraph below and add parentheses where appropriate.**

Every day, when I get home from school, I see Henry painting in his yard. He always paints outdoors his favorite painter also painted outdoors. Henry's cat is named Vincent after Vincent Van Gogh. Henry isn't a famous painter but he seems very happy.

C. **Write a short passage using parentheses.**

The Parrot and Mrs. Beardsley

A. **Insert colons where they belong in the letter below.**

Dear Animal Shelter

A parrot arrived on my doorstep at 300 PM yesterday.

I have never met a bird like it: he has extremely bad manners!

Has anybody lost a rude bird lately?

Sincerely,

Mrs. Beardsley

B. **Replace the conjunctions with semicolons in the passage below.**

Mrs. Beardsley didn't want to take the bird to the animal

shelter, because even though the bird had bad manners, it

was good company. The parrot and Mrs. Beardsley realized

they had many things in common, however, Mrs. Beardsley

knew that the friendship couldn't last.

The Stand-up

A.   Insert colons where they belong in the letter below.

Dear Mr. Gooch

I want to become a great stand-up comic. I saw your show last week, and everything about it was amazing your timing, your topics, your facial expressions. So here's my question what do I need to become a successful stand-up comic?

Sincerely,

Gary

B.   Replace the conjunctions with semicolons in the passage below.

Gary studied other comics, and he gathered jokes. He decided to test his act on Alex, his three-year-old brother. Alex found most things funny, so Gary should at least get lots of laughs. Even so, the first show with a real audience was a disaster: when Gary walked onstage, the audience pelted him with tomatoes!

Hiccups

A.   Insert colons where they belong in the letter below.

Dear Uncle Amit

This is urgent: how do you stop hiccups? I started

hiccupping at 700 p.m. last night, and I'm still going. I've

tried everything standing on my head, singing, drinking

water backward, and all three at the same time. Do you have

any other ideas?

Hic!

Moshim

B.   Replace the conjunctions with semicolons in the passage below.

Moshim thought he would spend the rest of his life

hiccupping. Maybe he would graduate hiccupping, and

he might even get married hiccupping. Then Moshim

remembered Uncle Amit's idea: a scary movie. Moshim

gulped because just thinking about it was terrifying! His

knees shook, and his skin prickled. Then he realized

something magical had happened...

The Lost City of Atlantis

A.   Insert colons where they belong in the letter below.

Dear Travel Agent

I recently heard about a beautiful city named Atlantis.
At 721 AM today, I had the best idea of my life I'm going to
travel to Atlantis! Therefore, I'd be grateful if you answered
my questions where exactly is the city located and how much
is a ticket to get there?

Sincerely,

Mrs. A. D. Venturer

B.   Replace the conjunctions with semicolons in the passage below.

A few days later, Mrs. Venturer learned that Atlantis
might not exist. People had looked for it in many different
places, for example, Antarctica, Indonesia, the Caribbean, and
Ireland. As Mrs. Venturer studied her maps, Bernard the dog
watched her anxiously because he wanted to go on vacation.

The City of the Future

A.   Read the passage. Identify and correct the errors.

What will a city of the future look like? Will it be filled with traffic smog and litter and will we have to travel for miles to sea a garden or a tree? If we take care of the Earth, here is what a city of the future might look like People will walk cycle or skate too work, however if they live too far away, they will take buses or drive cars that run on fuel made from plants. In the city of the future, there will be trees everywhere old airports and parking lots will be turned into peaceful parks. After work and on the weekends, people will walk and breath the fresh air in the city of the future, people will greet one another and smile

B.   Write a passage about a city you imagine in the future. Proofread it for correctness.

The Zoologist

A.   Read the passage. Identify and correct the errors.

dian fossey 1932–1985 loved animals. She trained to become an animal doctor, but after a trip to africa, she decides that the wild mountain gorilla were her passion. She studies gorillas in Zaire. Later, she started a gorilla study center in rwanda. She lives at the center for eighteen years with the gorillas.

To study the gorillas, Dian first has to gain there trust. She imitated their habits and sounds. Sometimes, she eats the same foods that they eat and slowly, the gorillas began to trusts her and Dian found that they had personalities just like people does.

B.   Write a passage about what animal you might like to study. Proofread it for correctness.

The Loudest Sound in the World

A.   Read the passage. Identify and correct the errors.

In 1883, a volcano erupted on the island of Krakatoa in indonesia. The explosion (which happened in august, was so loud that people in perth, australia, herd it, and people on an island 3,000 miles away feel the ground shake.

The eruption caused huge waves (called tsunamis, to crash into nearby islands. Some of the waves were 130 feat high and they killed many people. Other people was killed by the hot ash that shot from the volcano. About three hundred towns and villages disappeared. The island of Krakatoa were almost completely blown apart.

B.   Write a passage about something you know about natural disasters. Proofread it for correctness.

How to Save the Earth

A. **Read the passage. Identify and correct the errors.**

april 22 is Earth Day. Saving the Earth shouldnt be limited to won day each year, though! There is lots of small, simple things you can does every day. Here is a few ideas:

1. Instead of buying brand new school supplies, use the pens pencils and notebooks that you didnt use up last year.

2. When you wrap a gift, use the pages from old newspapers, magazines, or comics.

3. Save water by taking a quick shower rather than a bath youll get just as clean.

4. To save energy, switch off the lights when you left a room.

5. Try to by fruit and vegetables that arent rapped in plastic.

B. **Write a passage about something you do to save the earth. Proofread it for correctness.**